The world's great thinkers may meditate
On happiness and strife,
But it's Lucy who adds perspective
With her sharp outlook on life!

With Best Wishes from

The Eunash Family

Lucy Look

by Charles M. Schul

Hallmark

Contents

Other Peanuts Philosophers by Charles M. Schulz

THE MEDITATIONS OF LINUS
THE WIT AND WISDOM OF SNOOPY
CHARLIE BROWN'S REFLECTIONS

LINUS ON LIFE
SNOOPY'S PHILOSOPHY
THE WORLD ACCORDING TO LUCY
THE WISDOM OF CHARLIE BROWN

Editorial Direction: Arnold Shapiro
Design: William Hunt and David Jenkins